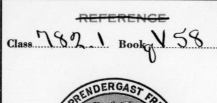

King of Egypt

Ramfis

Amonasro

Amneris

Aïda

Rhadames

AIDA

THE STORY OF VERDI'S GREATEST OPERA

Adapted by

ROBERT LAWRENCE

and

Illustrated by

BARRY BART

GROSSET & DUNLAP

Publishers   NEW YORK

Copyright, 1938, by The Metropolitan Opera Guild, Inc.

Foreword

THE METROPOLITAN OPERA GUILD, INC. is a group of people who themselves enjoy opera and believe that it may be of enjoyment to everyone. Since many operas are hard to follow unless we know what they are about, the Guild has been glad to prepare this book which will help you understand the ancient war between Egypt and Ethiopia as it touched Rhadames the soldier, Amneris the Princess, and Aïda the slave. These were far off times, but Verdi's music can bring them to life for us today, and give us a hint, even in the covers of this book, of the thrilling drama that is "Aïda."

Printed in the United States of America

About the Author

GIUSEPPE VERDI was a composer whose spirit never grew old. At the age of eighty he was still writing great music. This strength of purpose marked Verdi's whole career. In every new undertaking, he tried for something finer than he had done before. As a result, his art advanced steadily, reaching its peak in his three last operas: "Aïda," "Otello" and "Falstaff."

In the year 1869, Verdi received a strange offer from the Khedive of Egypt. The Khedive had built an opera house in the city of Cairo and wanted Verdi to compose a new work for this theatre. The payment would be large. There was only one condition attached; the new opera must have an Egyptian background. A famous French scholar was already searching the history of Egypt for a suitable story. His findings were to be dramatized and translated into Italian verse.

Verdi accepted this unusual commission and spent two years working on "Aïda." The first performance took place in Cairo in 1871. Since that time, "Aïda" has been presented all over the world under all sorts of conditions — in splendid opera houses, in sports arenas, in flood-lighted baseball parks, by starlight at the base of the Egyptian Pyramids. The pageantry and stirring drama of this opera are universal in their appeal.

[9]

Act One

BEFORE the curtain rises on "Aïda," the orchestral introduction tells us of the struggle we are to witness. For "Aïda," is a story of conflict — the conflict between love and duty.

Rhadames, an ambitious young warrior, is a faithful servant of Egypt, ready to answer his country's call. But he loves Aïda, a captive slave. She is a prize of war from the land that Egypt hates — Ethiopia. How can Rhadames serve his country and keep the love of Aïda?

Two opposing themes are heard in the prelude to the opera. One is the soft, pleading motive of Aïda:

The other motive, grave and solemn, is identified with the priests of Egypt, who guard the power and glory of the nation:

These themes struggle against each other, reaching a mighty climax.

[11]

As the music subsides, the motive of Aïda is heard once again, very softly, and the curtain rises.

We see a great hall in the palace of the King at Memphis. Young Rhadames is conversing with Ramphis, the High Priest of Egypt.

"Yes," Ramphis is saying, "I have heard that the Ethiopians are again invading the Nile. A messenger will soon be here with news."

"Have you consulted the goddess Isis?" asks Rhadames.

Ramphis, who interprets the signs of the gods, looks searchingly at Rhadames. "Isis has already chosen the leader of Egypt's army," he declares. "The new commander is young and brave. I shall announce his name to the King." Ramphis departs, and Rhadames is alone.

The young soldier's thoughts instantly turn to martial glory. "What if *I* have been chosen?" he exclaims. "What if my dreams were to come true! I could return to Memphis in triumph and say, 'It is for you, heavenly Aïda, that I have fought and conquered.'"

"CELESTE AÏDA" ("HEAVENLY AÏDA")

"Isis has already chosen the leader."

As Rhadames looks up from his reverie, he is surprised to see Amneris, the King's daughter, standing on the staircase of the palace. She has been watching him closely.

Amneris is madly in love with Rhadames. Why has he never returned her affection? Does he care for someone else? . . . These ideas haunt the princess, filling her mind with jealous schemes. She descends the stairs and approaches Rhadames.

"You are happy today," she remarks. "How fortunate is the woman who brings you such joy!"

Her prying words disturb Rhadames. "I have been dreaming of glory," he answers. "If only I were chosen by Isis to lead Egypt's army!"

"Do you always dream of glory?" asks Amneris. "Have you no other desires?"

Rhadames does not answer. How can he tell the princess that he is in love, not with her but with her slave, Aïda? His silence provokes Amneris to anger and suspicion. In the orchestra, we hear the motive of her jealousy:

This spiteful motive soon gives way to the soft, pleading theme of Aïda. The slave girl has timidly entered the hall. But why is Rhadames so agitated? Why is he looking so ardently at Aïda? "Can this slave be my rival?" wonders the princess. "I will question her and learn the truth!" Concealing her anger, she beckons invitingly to Aïda.

"Come here, Aïda. You know how I value your friendship. Confide in me—why are you weeping?"

"Alas," cries Aïda, "we are threatened with war. I weep for my country and yours."

"Is there nothing else?" persists Amneris. "Is there no deeper sorrow?"

A great trio follows, in which all three characters express their secret thoughts. Aïda weeps not so much for her country as for her love; Amneris sings of her jealousy, for she now suspects Aïda of being her rival; Rhadames fears that Amneris will wreck his fondest hopes.

Their stormy emotions are interrupted by the arrival of the King of Egypt. A great procession of priests and warriors, headed by Ramphis and the King, files into the palace. They have come to hear news of the war.

"Let the messenger approach!" orders the King.

A courier rushes in breathlessly. "The Ethiopians are invading the soil of Egypt!" he cries. "They have destroyed our fields and are marching on the city of Thebes. A fierce chieftain is leading them — Amonasro."

Aïda stifles a cry. Amonasro, the savage King of Ethiopia, is her *father*. Will he come at last to free her from her bondage? Taken captive in the last war and bound in slavery to Amneris, she has never revealed her identity to anyone in Egypt, not even to Rhadames.

"Let the messenger approach!"

"Our armies are pouring from the hundred gates of Thebes," continues the messenger, "and are giving battle to the enemy."

"Let death and destruction be our battle cry!" shouts the King.

The priests, led by Ramphis, clamor wildly for war. As the shouting dies, the King speaks solemnly: "Isis, the mighty goddess, has chosen our supreme commander — Rhadames! Go now to the temple of Vulcan, oh warrior, to receive the sacred armor of Egypt."

Rhadames is overjoyed at the King's decree. Amneris, too, is filled with pride. She hands him the royal standard, exclaiming, "Return victorious!" Everyone, even the captive Aïda, repeats the thrilling cry.

After Rhadames has departed for the temple of Vulcan, and Amneris and the others have gone, Aïda reproaches herself bitterly. "'Return victorious!' How can I repeat such words? My father and brothers are fighting to restore me to my country. Shall Rhadames conquer them, shall he be stained with their blood?"

In a patriotic fury, Aïda calls upon the gods to defeat and scatter the armies of Egypt. At the next moment she is seized with remorse, thinking of her lover. To whom ought she give her allegiance — to her country or to Rhadames? "Oh, you gods," she prays, "take pity on my suffering and let me die." These words are fitted to a beautiful, expressive melody:

As Aïda slowly crosses the great hall of the palace, the curtain falls.

* * * * *

The second scene of Act I takes place in the temple of Vulcan. Clouds of incense rise from the dimly lighted altar. Far off in the darkness, behind rows of mighty columns, the High Priestess is chanting a weird hymn to the great god Ptah:

As the priestesses circle about in a mysterious dance, Rhadames enters the temple. He has come to invoke the blessing of Ramphis. The young warrior kneels before the altar, and the High Priest gives him the sacred sword of Egypt, saying: "To you the gods entrust the fate of our nation. This divine sword, wielded by your hand, must bring terror, death to the enemy!"

Rhadames is now supreme commander of Egypt's forces. He rises, holding the sacred sword on high. The priests hail him, and a triumphant shout rings through the temple: "Almighty Ptah!"

"This sword must bring death to the enemy."

Act Two

THE PRAYER of Egypt has been granted — Rhadames is returning victorious. Great plans have been made to celebrate his triumph over the Ethiopians. The King, the priests, and the highest dignitaries of the land are to assemble before the gates of Thebes to honor the conquering hero.

As the curtain rises, Princess Amneris is preparing for her part in the celebration. She lies on a stately couch in her chamber, while her slaves adorn her with jewels and precious garments. A group of maid servants serenades the princess with praises of Rhadames. Amneris takes up the refrain, singing of her longing for the brave young warrior:

"Hasten your return, my beloved!"

To divert the princess on this long, sultry afternoon, a ballet of little Moorish slaves prances about the chamber in a strange, oriental dance. When they have finished, the maid servants resume the lilting rhythm of their serenade.

"I am your friend, Aida."

Amneris suddenly commands her attendants to be quiet. "Silence!" she orders. "I see Aïda coming. Child of the defeated, her grief is sacred to me." At a sign from the princess, the attendants withdraw.

For one brief moment, real pity has filled the heart of Amneris. But as Aïda enters the chamber, this pity turns to suspicion and jealousy. "Whenever I see her," thinks Amneris, "the most terrible doubts arise within me. I must find out her secret!"

To gain her purpose, she pretends to sympathize with Aïda. "Your people are defeated, Aïda. I wish I could do something to comfort you, to make you happy."

"How can I be happy, far from my native land?" Aïda answers sorrowfully. "Ah, if I could learn the fate of my father and my brothers!"

"No sorrow is lasting," says Amneris. "Time will heal your wounds; and, besides, there is the power of *love*." The princess watches Aïda intently as she mentions this word. Not the slightest movement of the unhappy slave girl escapes her.

"Come now, Aïda," she continues with feigned friendliness, "reveal your secret to me. Are you in love with one of our officers?"

Aïda trembles, fearful of her secret. "What do you mean?"

Staring fixedly at Aïda, Amneris exclaims, "Rhadames is dead, slain by your countrymen! Can you weep for him?"

"I shall weep forever!" moans Aïda.

In a seething rage, Amneris throws aside all pretense and reveals

the violence of her envy. "Tremble, you vile slave!" she shouts. "I spoke falsely only to test you. Rhadames lives!"

"He lives?" cries Aïda. "I thank you, O you gods!"

"Now I know your secret!" exclaims Amneris. "Yes, you love him, but so do I. Do you hear me? I am your rival—*I, the daughter of the Pharaohs.*"

Aïda is stung by these bitter taunts. She is about to tell the proud Egyptian that her own lineage is just as pure, that she is the daughter of the mighty Amonasro. But she restrains herself and begs for mercy. "You are happy," she pleads. "You are powerful. I have only my love. Take pity on my grief!"

"Never!" cries Amneris. "I feel no pity for you, only hatred and revenge."

Distant trumpet calls and the joyous shouting of the people reach the chamber. Rhadames is returning!

"Follow me, slave," commands Amneris. "You will see now if you can compete with me for his love. While you kneel in the dust, I shall ascend the throne of Egypt."

She strides haughtily from the chamber, and Aïda is left alone in her grief. With the same expressive melody which she had sung in the first act, the slave girl once more begs the gods for pity. Slowly and wearily, she turns and follows Amneris.

* * * * *

In the second scene of this act, the colossal entrance to the city of Thebes is thronged with people. They shout with enthusiasm as the King arrives and takes his place on an immense throne before the city gates. At his side is Amneris, dressed in regal splendor. Lonely and unnoticed in the midst of the procession, Aïda humbly follows the princess.

More and more people surge forward. Ramphis and the priests enter, singing their stern motive which we heard in the prelude to the first act. Then the victorious troops of Egypt parade past the King, while the trumpeters play this famous march:

At the climax of the march, a glittering ballet appears in the square, dancing jubilantly in celebration of Egypt's victory. Following the dancers come fresh companies of soldiers, bringing the spoils of war

"Hail, oh conquering hero!"

from Ethiopia — precious gold statues of the gods and other sacred objects which had belonged to the conquered. In their wake come the jubilant children of Thebes, waving palm branches. The crowd presses forward, eager to catch a glimpse of the returning hero. Excitement is running high — the supreme moment of victory is at hand! Finally, Rhadames arrives in a magnificent chariot drawn by milk-white horses. As he alights, the crowd roars its welcome and the King comes down from his throne to embrace the conqueror.

"Savior of your country," says the King, "Egypt salutes you! Come and receive the token of triumph from my daughter."

As Rhadames bows before Amneris, the princess tenderly places a laurel wreath on his brow.

"Ask whatever favor you wish, brave warrior," the King continues. "I swear by my crown that I will grant it. Nothing shall be denied you on this memorable day."

"First, O King," answers Rhadames, "let the prisoners be brought before you."

A sorrowful band of captives enters, their wrists bound in chains. Only one of the prisoners bears himself courageously. His eyes blaze defiantly as he is led before the gaping crowd. It is Amonasro, the savage King of Ethiopia, disguised as a regular officer of his own army.

"My father!" cries Aïda, running toward him.

"Say nothing!" whispers the prisoner . . . If the Egyptians ever suspected his identity, they would kill him at once!

"Step forward," commands the King of Egypt. "Who are you?"

"Aïda's father," replies Amonasro.

These are the only truthful words he utters. The rest of his answers are crafty lies, designed to mislead the Egyptians. "Our gallant King Amonasro is dead," he declares, "slain on the battlefield. We are conquered, O ruler of Egypt, and you are supreme. Have mercy on us!"

AMONASRO'S PLEA FOR MERCY

Aïda and all the Ethiopian prisoners join Amonasro in his plea. Deeply moved, the King of Egypt is on the point of granting their prayer. But Ramphis and the priests fiercely oppose any such mercy. "These people are enemies of Egypt," they cry. "Let them perish!"

Rhadames cannot endure seeing the terrible distress of Aïda. He approaches the foot of the throne. "You swore by your crown, O King, to grant me one favor. This I ask — release the prisoners!"

"O King, you are supreme. Have mercy!"

Ramphis and the priests object strenuously to this request. "If the Ethiopians are freed, they will strike again," claims the High Priest.

"Not so!" Rhadames answers. "Their leader, Amonasro, has been slain in battle. How can they hope to take revenge?"

"At least," argues Ramphis, "let us hold the father of Aïda as a pledge of their good faith. His presence here will assure peace and security."

The King of Egypt agrees with Ramphis. "I yield to your counsel," he declares. "And now, I propose an even greater bond of peace and security. Rhadames, the nation is indebted to you. The hand of my daughter Amneris shall be your reward. Some day you will both rule over Egypt."

Rhadames is appalled by these words of the King. He cannot protest; he has no other choice than to carry out the monarch's command. This reward, the most coveted honor in the land, makes him miserable. How can he live without Aïda?

The trumpets blare, and the procession prepares to enter the city. Egypt is victorious — Ethiopia completely crushed! Aïda can no longer hold back her grief. "Alas," she cries, "Rhadames will wed her and be lost to me forever! What hope is there left?"

"Take heart," whispers Amonasro. "Our country will soon be avenged on these Egyptians!"

The King of Egypt descends from his throne and passes through the gates of Thebes, hailed by his subjects. Amneris proudly follows him, arm in arm with her future consort. As the priests sing "Glory to Isis!" and the warriors march triumphantly into the city, Aïda falls weeping in the arms of her father.

Act Three

It is NIGHT on the banks of the Nile. From within the temple of Isis, half hidden by overhanging palm trees, comes the mysterious chanting of the priests. All else is silent. A boat containing Amneris and Ramphis draws up noiselessly to the shore.

The princess has come to pray to the goddess Isis on the eve of her wedding to Rhadames. Ramphis is at hand to guide her. As the weird chant of the priests fills the night air, Amneris and the High Priest climb the great staircase of the temple and disappear within the massive entrance.

For a moment, silence dominates the scene. Then we hear the motive of Aïda. The slave girl enters, heavily veiled. She is to meet Rhadames in this deserted place. At all costs, they must make sure that no one sees them together!

"What does Rhadames want to tell me?" she wonders. "If he comes to bid me farewell, I shall end my life in the depths of the Nile!"

A sad longing for her native land overwhelms Aïda. "Oh, my country," she cries, "I shall never see you again!" She thinks of the azure skies, the verdant hills of Ethiopia, and the orchestra plays a theme of melancholy beauty:

Andante mosso

Aïda's sadness grows more intense as she repeats, "Never, never again shall I behold you!"

Her solitude is suddenly disturbed by the sound of footsteps along the river bank. It is her father!

"I have come here for urgent reasons, Aïda," declares Amonasro. "You and Rhadames love each other. Why do you yield to your rival Amneris? If you wish, you can defeat her — you can have your throne and your love!"

In a glowing mood, Amonasro recalls the deep forests and fertile valleys of Ethiopia. "We shall see our land again!" he exclaims. "Our people have rearmed and are ready to strike at the Egyptians. There is only one piece of information necessary for our success. We must learn which road the enemy will take against us."

"But who could find that out?" asks Aïda.

"You!" her father answers. "Rhadames loves you. He commands the Egyptians. This is your chance!"

"Never!" she cries. "I will not betray Rhadames!"

Her refusal drives Amonasro into an overpowering fury. He reminds Aïda of how the Egyptians pillaged Ethiopia, burning the cities and slaughtering the inhabitants. "Ethiopia's dead will rise up to accuse you," he shouts. "Do you hear them? They are calling: *'Through you, our country has perished!'* And see — there in the shadows is your mother's ghost, raising her arms to curse you!"

In the greatest terror, Aïda cries, "No, father! Pity, pity!"

Hurling her to the ground, Amonasro thunders, "You are no daughter of mine! You are a slave of the Pharaohs!"

"No," she sobs, "I am still your daughter. Let me serve my country!"

Amonasro's wrath subsides as Aïda kneels before him. "Think!" he tells her. "Ethiopia will gain its freedom through your deed alone."

"Oh, my native land," exclaims Aïda, "how much suffering you have cost me!"

"Courage!" whispers Amonasro. "Rhadames is approaching. I shall hide among the trees and hear everything."

He disappears in the foliage and Aïda prepares for the wretched task of betraying her lover. Rhadames enters a moment later with a joyous greeting.

Aïda receives him coldly. "Why did you come here?" she asks. "Your love is pledged to Princess Amneris."

"What are you saying, Aïda?" he answers. "I love only you."

"How can you oppose the wishes of the King and the priests?" she asks bitterly.

"Listen, Aïda," replies Rhadames. "The Ethiopians are again invading our borders. I have been chosen to lead the army against them. If I am victorious, this time I shall ask for your hand as my reward."

"But don't you fear the anger of Amneris?" demands Aïda. "She would revenge herself upon my father and me. If you really love me, there is only one path open for us — we must flee!"

Aïda describes for him the fragrant forests of Ethiopia, filled with perfumed flowers. There, they could forget the world and live in perfect happiness. "Escape with me!" she urges softly.

"Come to the temple of Isis."

"No!" declares Rhadames. "I cannot abandon my country!"

"You cannot?" cries Aïda. "Then stay in Egypt — watch them slay my father and myself!"

Rhadames is terrified at the thought that any harm might come to Aïda. "Never!" he shouts. "We will flee!"

The lovers embrace. They are ready to depart, when Aïda pauses in front of the clump of trees where her father is hiding. "Tell me," she asks Rhadames. "Which road can we take to avoid meeting the soldiers?"

"Our army will not march against the Ethiopians until tomorrow," he answers. "Tonight the road is clear. We can flee by the gorge of Napata."

"The gorge of Napata!" exclaims a voice in the darkness behind them. "My men will be there!"

"Who has overheard us?" cries Rhadames.

Aïda's father steps from his hiding place. "It is I, Amonasro, King of Ethiopia."

"You are Amonasro?" Rhadames is stunned by this news. He had believed Amonasro to be dead, killed in battle. *"You* — the King?" Rhadames now realizes that he has given military information to the enemy. "I have betrayed my country!" he shouts. "I am dishonored!"

"No, you are not guilty," says Amonasro in an effort to console him. "Come with us; our army is waiting. Aïda's love will be your reward. Come!" With the help of Aïda, he tries to drag Rhadames away.

A cry from the steps of the temple shatters the stillness of the night: "Traitor!"

It is Amneris. She has overheard them!

"So you have come to spoil our plans!" yells Amonasro. "Die then!" He rushes at the princess with drawn dagger, but Rhadames bars his way. "Be quick!" warns Rhadames. "You and Aïda must flee!"

Hearing the uproar, the High Priest has appeared in the entrance of the temple with a guard of soldiers. He is in time to see Aïda and her father retreating into the dense underbrush of the Nile. "Follow them!" he orders.

Rhadames remains behind to face his punishment. Advancing toward the High Priest, he holds out the sacred sword of Egypt. "Priest of Isis," he declares, "I surrender my command." As Ramphis takes the sword from the disgraced warrior, the curtain falls.

"I am ready to die."

Act Four

THE PRINCESS AMNERIS strides despairingly through the corridors of the King's palace. She has learned that Rhadames is to be led to judgment and certain death. All of her envy is swept aside by her love and pity for the warrior. Determined to save him, she orders him to be brought before her.

As Rhadames appears, Amneris begs him to confess his guilt and ask for mercy. "I am not guilty," he replies. "I was thoughtless enough to reveal military information, but I did not intend to betray my country."

"Then live and clear yourself!" cries Amneris, "Live for *me!* I would give up my throne, my country, my life for your love!"

"I have already sacrificed everything I hold dear for Aïda," Rhadames replies.

"Speak no more of her!" exclaims Amneris, with rising anger.

Rhadames is sure that the vengeful princess has killed Aïda. "Where is she?" he asks anxiously. "What have you done with her?"

"I have not killed Aïda," answers Amneris. "I would never commit

"Rhadames! You have betrayed your country."

such a deed! Her father was slain by our soldiers, but Aïda escaped. No one knows where she is."

"May the gods guide her back to her native land!" cries Rhadames.

"Promise me, Rhadames," insists Amneris, "that you will never try to find her. If you pledge me your word, I shall appeal to the King himself to save you. Once you fall into the hands of the priests, you are lost!"

Rhadames resolutely refuses her offer. "Death has no terrors for me," he declares. "I fear it less than your pity."

He returns to his prison cell and Amneris is left alone in the corridor. Her jealousy returns like a nightmare to torture her. It has been through *her* spite, *her* envy that the man she loves is about to die.

As the stern, solemn motive of the priests of Egypt is announced by the orchestra, Ramphis and his followers cross the corridor. Slowly and gravely they descend the narrow staircase which leads to the underground hall of judgment. Rhadames is escorted down the stairs under close guard. "Ah, who can save him now?" cries Amneris.

From far beneath the corridor, the accusing voice of the High Priest is heard. "Rhadames! Rhadames! Rhadames!" he is saying. "You have betrayed the secrets of your country to the enemy; you have deserted your camp the day before the battle; you have been a traitor to your King, to your country, to your vows. Defend yourself!"

There is a long, terrible silence. The doomed man does not answer. Amneris, who is peering through a grating into the judgment hall below, breaks out in wild lamentations. "Spare him!" she cries. "You gods, have pity!"

The hollow voices of the priests pronounce the warrior's punishment. "Rhadames," they proclaim, "a traitor's death awaits you. You shall be buried alive beneath the altar of the goddess whose vows you have broken!"

Amneris shrieks as she hears this awful sentence. The priests climb the staircase, exclaiming, "The traitor!" In one last desperate attempt, the princess pleads for the life of Rhadames. The priests spurn her, saying, "He has betrayed his country; he must die."

Half crazed with grief and remorse, Amneris rushes after them and screams: "Cruel priests of Egypt, I curse you! May the vengeance of heaven destroy you all!" In a frenzy of emotion, she falls fainting to the ground.

* * * * *

The final scene of the opera takes place in the temple of Vulcan. We see a great hall with golden walls and, far beneath, the gloomy vault in which Rhadames is to meet his doom. Two priests are lowering the fatal stone which seals the tomb.

Rhadames sits despondently within the vault. "I shall never see Aïda again," he thinks. "Oh, Aïda, where are you now? I hope that you will never learn my fate!"

Suddenly, he hears something moving in the murky blackness. Panic seizes him. "Is it a ghost?" he cries. "A vision?"

Aïda emerges from the darkness of the tomb. "It is I," she answers. "I have come back to die with you."

"To die!" exclaims Rhadames. "In the flower of your youth?"

The weird chanting of the priests penetrates the stillness of the tomb: "Almighty Ptah, Almighty Ptah!" The sound maddens Rhadames. With a supreme effort, he tries to lift the fatal stone.

"In vain," says Aïda. "All is over for us on earth. Our troubles will end only beyond this life."

With quiet resignation, the lovers bid farewell to earth.

"O TERRA ADDIO" ("FAREWELL TO EARTH")

Princess Amneris appears in the temple above, dressed in deepest mourning. Choking with grief, she kneels on the stone that seals the vault, and prays for the peace of Rhadames' soul. In the darkness below, Rhadames and Aïda sink into each other's arms in a last, dying embrace.

"Farewell, oh earth!"

Suggested Recordings of "Aida"

1. The complete opera: Victor Musical Masterpieces—Album 54.

2. "Celeste Aida" ("Heavenly Aida"): Victor-7770.

3. "Ritorna Vincitor" ("Return Victorious"): Victor-7106.

4. The Temple Scene (Act I), Duet of Ramphis and Rhadames, with chorus of the priests: Victor-8111.

5. Grand march (Triumphal Scene, Act II): Victor-11885, Parlophone-E11041.

6. Ballet music (Act II): Polydor-66584.

7. "O Patria Mia" ("My Native Land"): Victor-7770. ("Ritorna Vincitor" on the reverse side.)

8. Duet of Aida and Amonasro (Act III). (Amonasro induces Aida to betray Rhadames): Victor-8207.

9. Duet of Rhadames and Aida (Act III). (Rhadames agrees to flee with Aida): Victor-8160.

10. Finale of Act III: Victor-8206. (Trio of Aida, Rhadames, and Amonasro.)

11. Duet of Amneris and Rhadames (Act IV, Scene 1): Polydor-66819. (Amneris offers to save Rhadames' life if he will abandon Aida.)

12. "O Terra Addio" ("Farewell to Earth") and Finale, Act IV: Victor-3040 and 3041.

782.1   gV 58

Oct 2 '44			
Feb 10 '45			
Feb 29			
Apr 19 '46			
Apr 16 '47			
APR 30			
Jun 7 '48			
Aug 14 '48			
Apr 5 '49			
Apr 18 30			
Jul 19 '51			
Mar 8 '52			
AUG 4 '34			